W9-CFJ-949

IT'S AUTUMN!

IT'S AUTUMN!

Text
and
Photographs
by
SISTER NOEMI WEYGANT, O.S.B.

THE WESTMINSTER PRESS
Philadelphia

COPYRIGHT © MCMLXVIII SISTER NOEMI WEYGANT, O.S.B.

All rights reserved — no part of this book may be reproduced in any form without permission in writing from the publisher, except by a reviewer who wishes to quote brief passages in connection with a review in magazine or newspaper.

LIBRARY OF CONGRESS CATALOG CARD No. 68-18782

BOOK DESIGN BY
DOROTHY ALDEN SMITH

Published by The Westminster Press ®
Philadelphia, Pennsylvania

PRINTED IN THE UNITED STATES OF AMERICA

CONTENTS

A PRECIOUS GIFT

WE ARE BORN with a sense of wonder at the miracle of life. The world of childhood is one of fantasy and hidden meanings, the out-of-doors peopled with elves and fairies. These imaginings are part of what children see and feel, and life to them is full of richness and excitement, all this an inheritance from the misty background of the race.

The tragedy of the modern world is that this innate awareness of nature is swiftly lost in our divorcement from the earth. If the age of delight and spiritual oneness can be preserved even into adulthood, it will do much toward filling the emptiness and countering the despair of those who have severed their roots with the past.

Sister Noemi, through her sensitivity expressed so hauntingly in poetry and pictures, has caught this age of fantasy, the pure and simple joy of a child looking at its world. When she portrays a spider web caught on a blade of grass, she sees a rainbow bent; when she looks at the frosty, blowing world of autumn, she invites you to walk with her and join the swirling dance of leaves and vines; she wonders if a dried and drooping poppy pod could be a fringed lamp streaming with light or perhaps a little hat. A crimson whirling ginseng beckons her to ride into the blue like an astronaut. Gaily she shouts: "Put on your Indian feet. . . . Let us go for a walk together. . . . The day is free and God is good." She speaks to a frog and asks, "Who are you and who am I?" posing the eternal question of man.

In this lovely book of poems and photographs she sees the beautiful in common things, touches a chord that is anchored in deep and universal meaning. Hers is a rare and precious gift, for she has eyes that see, a mind full of love, and an artistry that is timeless.

Sigurd F. Olson

AN INVITATION

Let us go
   for a walk together,
     in the frost,
     in the sun,
     by the meadow,
     down the hills,
     around the lake,
     along a river.

Come, come . . .
The day is free
   and God is good.
He awaits us
     in the fields,
     in the woods.

Now we walk,
     now we run,
     now we jump,
     now we stop.

OH! . . .

LIKE A RAINBOW BENT

Drop to your knees
   by the cattail reeds!
May be a bit wet,
   but nevermind.
A little wet
   won't hurt you,

                    but see!

A spider
   has used
      a bending, golden blade
   as a frame
      on which to weave
      his silver web.
Now it is pearled
   with dew.

But . . .
   you'll have to look

                  quick,

   for already the sun
      is finding it.

Soon
   it will be dry
   and vanish . . .
      like a rainbow
      from the sky.

THE TIME IS AUTUMN

Autumn is the time
  when nature makes ready
    for bed.
But before everything
  goes to sleep,
  autumn takes part
    in a play.

Nothing on TV
  or in the movies
  can compare
    to what awaits you—
        out there.

And many things,
  too,
  will speak to you,
  if you . . .
        listen.

So here is the arrow
  that points the way.

Are you looking?

Are you listening?

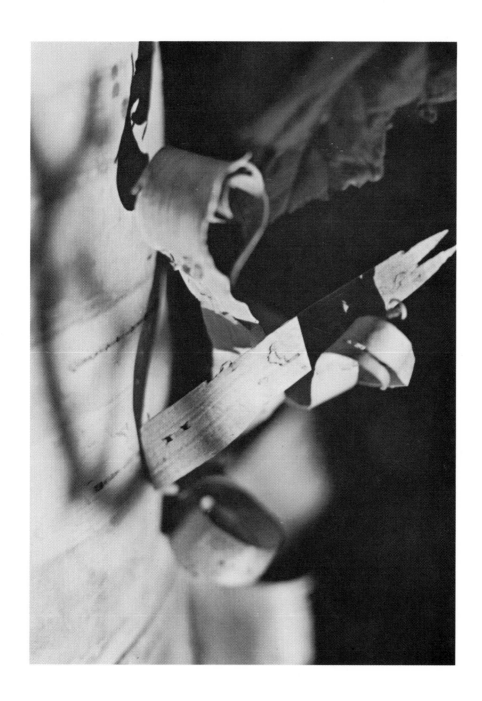

I'M THE AUTUMN BANNER

I don't know
   what happened
   to the other half of me,
      and I'm too happy
      a little fern,
      really to care.

For I'm no longer
   a hidden
   forest frond,
   but a flag
      blowing gaily
      in the wind,
   letting all who see me
      know,
      it's on with the show.

So, come on—
Come on in
   and revel
      in
      autumn pageantry.

WHAT DO YOU WANT?

Funny face
   with big eyes
      out here on a log!

Are you trying
   to scare me
      with a Halloween prank?

Or is it that you
   want me
   to play peekaboo
      with you?

HAVE A RIDE WITH ME?

Hello!
Hello,
   my small friends!

Grown-ups,
   having no imagination,
     tell me I'm a variety
     of wild aster.
But you and I
   know better.

I'm really a plane
   with green-and-red wings,
     about to take off,
     with a rhyme and a sing,
     to some other
     nature-sphere.

Want to fly along with me?

You can sit
   on the little leaf,
     right beneath
     my white-bright propellers.

19

WHO ARE WE?

We'll tell you
  who we are.

We're little brown men
  who live
    in the thick of the forest.

Our huts are built
  up and down
  the sides
  of a big stump,
    which is to us
    big as a mountain
    in Switzerland.

We feed on the wood
  and dance on moss
  that grows soft and green
    on the ground,
    and all around.

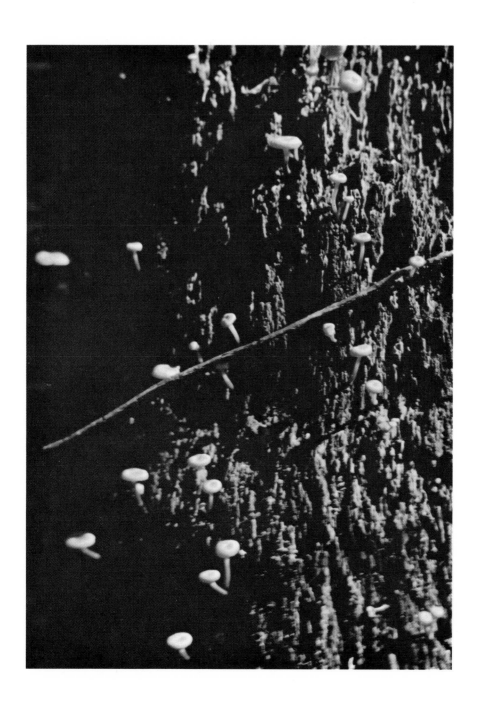

AS YOU CAN SEE

I'm a lazy,
   hazy,
   autumn turtle,
     soaking up the sun.

When autumn is done,
   I'll dive
   into the lake

     and hibernate.

So—
I'll see you
   in the spring,
   if everything
   goes well with me,
     during the winter freeze.

HOW ABOUT ME?

You delight in me
   because in the sunlight
   I shine like a star.
Nevertheless, I'm a fake.

I'm not from the sky,
   but I am the fruit
   of the wild cucumber.

   Though I look dangerous,
   if you touch me,
     you'll find out
     my spines are too weak
     even to prick you.
And though I may look
     as if I might hold
     something to eat,
   I'm empty inside
      except for a few seeds
     that squirt out from the bottom
     in autumn.

My body is round and spongy
   like a rubber ball,
     but I don't bounce.
I hang to my vine all winter,
   turning dark brown
   with time.
But . . .
   though I rattle in the wind
   like a ghost,
I don't scare
   even the small forest folk.

JOIN OUR DANCE

The pumpkins we grew
   were cut
   from our vines.
So left behind
   as skeletons,
     we go into
      a Halloween dance.

The leaves
   come flying
     through our weavings.

Put on
   your Indian feet.
Join our beat,
   beat, beat, beat,
   as round and round
   we go
     in the autumn sun,
     in the autumn blow.

WHAT HAVE WE HERE?

I know what you're thinking—
   the mouths of ducks
   are upside down,
   and five of them here
   are waiting for you
     to throw in food.

But that isn't so.

This is how a duck dives
   for something he "I-spies"
   under the water
     to eat.
And his tail opens up
   to give him balance
     while he feeds.

Right now,
   these ducks,
   which were ducklings
   last spring,
     are fattening up
     for a long flight south.

When they come back next year,
   they'll make homes
     for new ducklings
     of their own.

YES, LOOKS DECEIVE

When you look at me,
   you want to say,
"Can't be so.
Grass is always green."

      Well,
   when the cold
   and glow
   of autumn come,
I open up into
   a lacy, lazy
   Japanese fan,
      tinted pink and rose.

HUSH!

Hush!

A deer has just passed by.

For all we know,
  he's looking at us
  from the deep of the woods,
  with big, soft eyes.

I'M WAITING—

I was a tomato,
   ripe and sweet,
   then,
   before I could be picked
   or eaten,
      the frost came
      and stole my fruit.

Now says
   my brown vine,
"You're a useless
   old skin.
Drop to the ground."

But I keep thinking—
   maybe if I wait,
   a little boy
   will find me
      and use me
      for a marble bag.

AUTUMN ACCIDENT

Oh! Oh!
What mischief have we here?

Where a little spider
   spun his web
   for catching
   a mosquito
   or a fly,
      he captured, instead,
      a hundred-hundred
      fluffy white
      grass pollens
      which nature set free
      to carry seed!

Well—a spider
   can't eat them.
He'll have to go hungry
   until he can spin
   a new web
      all over again.

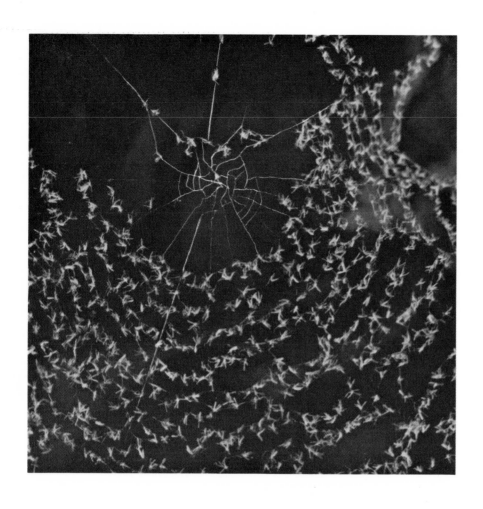

WHERE ARE YOU?

Dear wild bird,
   where have you gone?

Your feather lies
   so frail and white
      on stones
       orange with fungi.

I look and look
   from all sides
   into the sky
  and out over the lake,
      but I cannot see you
      anywhere . . .

Dear wild bird—
   your feather makes me lonely.

Where are you now?
I miss your song.

LOOK FOR ME NEXT SUMMER

I'm an autumn seed,
   with a light, white parachute.

I'm waiting
   for a takeoff
   in the first breeze
   for good flying
     that comes along.

Where will I land?
There is no knowing.

But if you're on the watch
   in the fields
   next summer,
     and come across
     a milkweed growing . . .

Well,
   maybe
     it's
     me.

ARE WE NOT BEAUTIFUL?

All summer long
  we grow
  in a mud-dy,
  goo-ey,
    some kind of bog.

Everyone passing by,
  looks at us with disgust,
    as if we enjoyed
    our ugliness
    and isolation.

Then comes fall.

Our floor dries,
  hardens.
Children walk in,
  laughing,
  pick our cattails,
  and every weed and blade
  combines
    to make a picture
    green and gold.

People driving by
  exclaim—
                    "OH!"

WE'RE KITTENISH

Kitten furry,
   kitten soft,
   kitten shine,
   kitten cuddly
are we,
    the pods
    of the wild lupine.

We twist and curl
   in our play,
    until all our seeds
    have dropped away.

WE'RE OLD-TIME DUSTERS

We're just as busy
    as we can be,
        dusting up the forest.

My, it does get so untidy
    in the fall,
        seeds and leaves
        and pods,
        and sticks,
        and feathers,
    and all sorts of weather
        to wet and blow.

One thing about winter—
        it's
        clean!

RED WHEELS

Red wheels spin up
   into the sky.

Are they windmills?

No,
   that was too long ago.

Must be,
   nature is about
   to conduct
   her own experiments
    in space.

HAVE PITY ON ME!

Pity me.
I was meant to bloom
   into a big,
   glorious,
   golden member
     of the daisy family.

Yes, it's true,
   all my elders
   kept telling me,
     "Hurry up! Hurry up!"

But no, I thought,
   I'll take my time.

Then came the frost.

Now I'm entrapped.
There is not enough sap
   in my stem
     to give the petals
     the strength
     and nourishment
     they need
     for flowering.

Soon the snow will come,
   and I'll never have time
     to grow up.

I HAVE A SECRET

I'm not a witch.
I'm still
   the lovely fern
   you used for a fairy wand
     last summer.

Then came the cold.

Arthritis set in.
My limbs break
   in the very wind
   through which they flowed
   so gracefully,
     and my fronds,
     so green and long
     and airy
     in summer,
     are curling up,
     stiffening,
     becoming brown.

But don't be sad.
It's October now,
   time for resting.

And I have a secret.

In the roots of me,
   sweet spring
     is safely nesting.

SOMETHING THERE IS ABOUT A BIRD'S NEST

See what lies here
   midst the debris
   of autumn leaf, fungi,
   and wild berries,
   black and dry!

A bird's nest.

Something there is about a bird's nest
   that is holy,
     for it was built for eggs,
     and a mother nesting,
   and it became a home,
     when the eggs hatched out,
      for bird babies,
      until they were grown.

We could carry it back with us,
   but a nest doesn't belong
     inside.

A nest belongs to the woodlands,
   like the bird
     and the wild bird song.

So let us leave it here, where it fell.

Brown pine needles dropping into it,
   and autumn leaves blowing,
   will soon cover it over,
     and then the snow,
      white,
      and light . . .

I WONDER

I wonder—
   is this old knot
   shedding tears
      because winter
      is nearly here?

You say,
   of course not.
This is a pine tree,
   and pine trees love winter
      especially.

But why is it crying?

I'M READY—ARE YOU?

Did you know
    that tomahawks grow?

Well, here I am,
    bright as gold,
    light as straw,
      eager to play.

Only—
    don't delay too long,
    for I'm here
    only in the fall,
      and only for
      a short time.

The next hard wind,
I dare say,
    will carry me away.

I HAVE GOOD USES

"Don't fool yourself,"
  a big bold flower said to me.
"You're only
  an old pod
  empty of seed,
    and about to drop off
    your stem."

I'm not
  just that!
I'm a lamp
  with a fancy fringe,
    and my light
    is shining down
    straight
    and bright.

The only warning I would give
  is this:
Don't try to move me
  to some other part
  of nature's room
  or—
    I might drop off
    at that.

But now I have another thought—
  if I do,
    you can use me
    for a hat.

HERE COMES WINTER

Last night
   there was a cold rain.
Everything this morning
   is . . .
      freeze.

Rain on the leaves
   has made them
      ice logs,
      aglow with light.
But they won't burn,
   for there is no sun,
      and in the air
      there is a bite.

And driving in from the north
   comes a big, dark cloud.
A big, dark truck,
   dumping snow galore
      on people,
      town,
      and forest floor.

When it reaches us . . .

Here it comes!
Can you catch a snowflake
   on your tongue?